For Conor and Sadhbh
ED and JG

For Kate Janaki (Ella) and Dara Luca
SK

Aoife - the facts

The name Aoife or Aife is taken from the Irish, meaning pleasant, radiant or beautiful. It may be associated with and derived from the ancient Gaulish goddess, Epona. The most common anglicized version is Eva.

The name was borne by many legendary heroines of Celtic mythology, most of whom had very strong associations with animals and birds. By far the best known Aoife is the third wife of Lir. A jealous stepmother she transforms the children of the king and her dead sister into swans, to wander the waterways of Ireland for 900 years. As punishment she herself is changed into a 'demon of the air' to live in dark clouds forever, by Lir or by her father according to different versions. Her account is told in detail in *The Tragic Story of the Children of Lir*, the so-called second sorrow of storytelling in Celtic mythology. Our story gives Aoife's version for the first time!

A second Aoife, a warrior chieftainess, lived in the time of Cuchulainn. She was a lover of animals and horses in particular. Sections of her story are detailed in *The Tragic Death of Aife's only Son,* a foretale to *Tain Bo Cuailnge*

(The Cattle Raid of Cooley). This Aoife provides the clearest linkages to the continental goddess, Epona, found in inscriptions and statues in France and later Britain. Epona was usually depicted on horseback, accompanied by a swan or riding a large horned goose. The only Celtic goddess worshipped in the Roman empire, she had a special feast day on Dec.18th. This worship seems to have been imported to Britain with Roman occupation, and may have transferred to Ireland as Aoife.

A third Aoife lived for a time as an amphibian in the realm of the Celtic sea god, Manannan Mac Lir. Later, on land she is transformed into a crane by a jealous lover. On her death her skin was made into the legendary Crane Bag of Irish tradition. This was variously believed to contain marvellous treasures including the letters of the ancient Ogham alphabet, inscriptions of which have been found principally in Cork and Kerry in Ireland and in Wales, Scotland, Cornwall and the Isle of Man.

Another Aoife, daughter of Abartach from the Fenian cycle, was changed into a heron by a jealous rival. The most recent legendary Aoife was a daughter of the king of Connaught. She is said to have had her marriage arranged by St Patrick.

Once there was a girl called Aoife. She was a very beautiful and pleasant girl.

Her dad was a brave and handsome warrior. Every day she asked to go riding on his horse. Sometimes, when the weather was warm and there were no clouds in the sky, he would take her with him on his horse through the forest.

During these trips Aoife learned about the many other living things in our world. Like birds that can fly against the strongest wind. Animals that can see in the dark. Butterflies that drink honey from flowers. Giant oak trees that grow high into the sky and live almost forever.

Her father taught her that all living things are our cousins. No matter how small, they have a place in this world and not one that is hurt can be replaced.

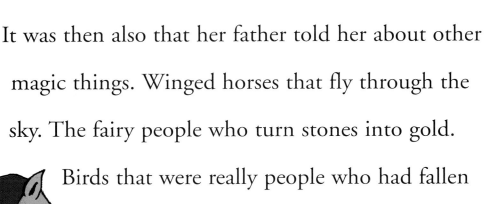

It was then also that her father told her about other magic things. Winged horses that fly through the sky. The fairy people who turn stones into gold. Birds that were really people who had fallen under a wicked witch's spell.

He taught her the special magic of talking to animals, birds and plants.

"When I grow bigger I will run as fast as a horse and I will fly to the clouds like a bird," thought Aoife.

Of course Aoife could not run as fast as a horse or fly as high as a bird, though she tried.

Once she raced her horse to a piece of carrot cake at the end of the garden.

Alas, when she got there the horse was licking its lips and the cake was nowhere to be seen!

Then she decided to fly to a cloud moving overhead. She waved her arms and jumped from the ground but landed in a puddle of water instead. "I guess I'm not really meant to fly," she said, as she picked herself up.

Aoife, however, did grow to love all wild things more and more. She was sure that they understood when she talked to them.

As she grew older she would go riding each day on her favourite white horse. Her pet swan would fly beside her. She could not fly but when the wind was in her hair she would close her eyes. Aoife would pretend.....

Some time later the king of the land was hunting with his hounds. He saw Aoife on her horse. "She is so beautiful I will make her my princess," he said. It was then that Aoife became Princess Aoife!

Now the king also had children whom he loved dearly. He spent so much time with them that Aoife became a little jealous. One day when the king was out hunting she decided to practice the magic taught to her by her father. She waved her wand and - whoosh!!! - the children were turned into the most beautiful swans.

"I think King Lir will be pleased to see you. I will never be able to fly but now you can fly higher than any bird and are more beautiful than any person," she said.

Alas, the king was not pleased. "Turn my children back into people at once!" he shouted. Poor Aoife did not know enough magic to turn them back. The king was very cross. "Then you also shall become a bird," he said.

With one wave of his wand she was transformed. Her long dark hair became the black feathers of a raven.

After a moment Aoife spread her wings. She soared into the sky. Higher and higher she flew. The breeze carried her to a place far above the land below.

Aoife smiled. Her dream to fly to the clouds had come true at last!

What's in a name?

Usually centuries of history, religious or legendary tradition.

The main source of names is in religious history, in the names of saints (Catherine) and, post Reformation, in the *Bible* and *Old Testament* in particular (Sarah and Adam). The *Koran* provides additional perspective on many of these names.

Names from Celtic legend, like Conor, have recently gained increased attention internationally.

Another source is classical, from pagan, royal or literary figures, e.g. Lawrence (Latin) and Chloe (Greek literature). Historical figures, such as Victoria, also provide a rich source.

Then there's Jack! It probably deserves a category all of its own having appeared from nowhere - but perhaps from Jankin, a version of John - to become the ubiquitous name in fairy tales and now a highly popular first name.

Recently parents have become much more adventurous. This follows the decrease in family and religious bonds that resulted in names passing from generation to generation. Increased access to other cultures has led to 'name globalisation', with names like Tanya, Brooklyn and Chelsea now more popular.

Other names recall a particular individual or event. The *Bible* and *Koran* name,